# Creative Mat. Age 7-9

# David Kirkby

Illustrations by Philip Hodgson.

First published 1992 by Folens Limited, Dunstable and Dublin.

ISBN 1 85276339 6

Folens Limited, Albert House, Apex Business Centre, Boscombe Road, Dunstable LU5 4RL, England.

Printed by Ashford Colour Press.

# Creative Maths Age 7-9

## Structure

# Teacher's Notes

## Themes

### Creative Maths 5-7

Colouring
Dice
Sequences and
Ordering
Matching
Dominoes
Pairs
Taking

### Creative Maths 7-9

Words
Squares
Arrangements
Calendars
Three
Pathways
Dice
Calculators

### Creative Maths 9-11

Dice
Triangles
Multiplying
Cubes
Frogs
Operations
Codes
Dates
Counters

### Sports Maths 7-9

Tennis
Swimming
Football
Cricket
Snooker
Athletics

### Sports Maths 9-11

Tennis
Swimming
Football
Cricket
Snooker
Athletics

# Teacher's Notes

**5. CALCULATOR STORY**
Solving problems using a calculator. (N3)
Selecting materials and mathematics to use for a task. (UA3/4)

**6. MEMORIES**
Collecting and ordering discrete data. (DH4)
Constructing and interpreting graphs. (DH2/3)
Recording findings and presenting them. (UA4/5)
Selecting the materials and mathematics for a task. (UA3/4)
Planning work methodically.

**7. WORDSCORE**
Adding mentally several single digit numbers. Adding two digit numbers. (N4)
Recording results in a table. (DH2/3)
Selecting mathematics to use for a task. Working methodically. (UA3/4)

**8. WORD LISTS**
Collecting, recording data leading to a frequency table. (DH2)
Constructing and interpreting graphs. (DH2/3)
Planning work methodically. Recording findings and presenting them. (UA3/4)

**9. WORD GAME**
Addition skills. Using a calculator to solve number problems. (UA3/4)
Recording results in a table. (DH2)
Select materials and mathematics. Plan methodically.
Record findings and present them. (UA3/4/5)

**10. MULTIPLICATION SQUARE**
Explaining and predicting number patterns. (A3)
Generalising, in words, patterns in number. (A4)
Multiplication facts up to 10x10. (N4)

**11. MISSING NUMBERS**
Explaining and predicting number patterns. (A3)
Multiplication facts up to 10x10. (N4)

**12. CUTTING UP SQUARES**
Recognising different shapes. Sorting them. (S2)
Understanding congruence of simple shapes. (S4)
Classifying types of quadrilaterals. (S6)
Selecting the materials and mathematics for a task. Planning methodically. (UA3/4/5)
Recording findings and presenting them. (UA3/4)

**13. STARS**
Sorting 2D shapes. Recognising symmetry. (S3)
Selecting the materials and mathematics for a task. Planning methodically. (UA3/4/5)
Recording findings and presenting them. (UA3/4)

**14. SQUARE SHAPES**
Finding areas and perimeters of simple shapes. (S4)
Sorting 2D shapes. (S3)
Selecting the materials and mathematics for a task. (UA3/4/5)
Record findings and present them. (UA3/4/5)

**15. ROWS AND COLUMNS**
Selecting the materials and mathematics for a task. (UA3/4/5)
Checking results. Planning methodically. (UA3/4/5)

**16. COUNTER ARRANGEMENTS**
Selecting materials and mathematics for a task. Planning methodically. (UA3/4/5/6)
Recording findings and presenting them.
Recording systemmatically. Breaking tasks into smaller ones. (UA3/4/5)

**17. COUNTER SHAPES**
Multiplication facts. (N3/4)
Patterns in number. (A3/4)
Recognising patterns in numbers through spatial arrangements. (A5)
Multiples and primes.

**18. REVERSALS**
Addition and subtraction of two and three digit numbers. (N4)
Pattern in number. (A3/4)
Recording and presenting findings. Generalisation. (UA3/4/5)

**19. RECTANGLE GAME**
Recognising types of movement. Rectangles. (S2)
Working methodically. Reviewing progress. (UA3/4/5)

**20. LINE-UP**
Recognising straight lines in different directions. (S1/2)
Working methodically. Predicting strategies and testing them. (UA3/4/5)

**21. BIRTHDAY MONTH**
Patterns in number. (A3/4)
Collecting, ordering discrete data. Presenting and interpreting results. (DH2/3/4)

**22. CALENDAR GAPS**
Patterns in number. Multiples. (A3/4)
Odd and even numbers. (A2)
Multiplication facts. (N3/4)

**23. CALENDAR JIGSAW**
Number patterns. (A3/4)
Recognise patterns in number through spatial arrangements. (A5)
Select materials and mathematics for a practical task. (UA3/4/5)

**24. DIAGONALS**
Addition of two digit numbers. Solving number problems. (N3/4)
Number patterns. (A3/4)
Select materials and mathematics for a task. Plan methodically. (UA3/4/5)
Record and present results.

**25. RECTANGLE CORNERS**
Addition of two digit numbers. Solving number problems. (N3/4)
Number patterns. (A3/4)
Select materials and mathematics for a task. Plan methodically.
Record and present results. (UA3/4/5)

**26. CALENDAR TOTALS**
Addition of two digit numbers. Solving number problems. (N3/4)
Number patterns. (A3/4)
Select materials and mathematics for a task. Plan methodically.
Record and present results. (UA3/4/5)

**27. THREE CIRCLES**
Addition of several single digit numbers. (N3)
Patterns in addition. (A3/4)
Recording systemmatically. Planning methodically. Checking results. (UA3/4/5)

**28. THREE IN A LINE**
Addition facts. (N2/3)
Recognising straight lines in different directions. (S1/2)

**29. MAKING NUMBERS**
Addition and subtraction facts. (N2/3)
Division of whole numbers. (N3)

**30. THREE STAMPS**
Addition of three single digit numbers. Subtraction. (N3)
Solving money problems. (N3/4)
Recording systemmatically. Planning methodically. (UA3/4/5)

**31. THREE MORE STAMPS**
Addition of three single digit numbers. (N3)
Solving money problems. (N3/4)

**32. THREE DIGITS**
Ordering numbers up to 1000. (N3)

**33. THREE DARTS**
Addition of several single digit numbers. (N3/4)
Selecting the mathematics for a task. Record and present findings. (UA3/4/5)

**34. STEPPING STONES**
Using negative numbers. Addition. (N5)
Planning work methodically. Recording systemmatically. (UA3/4/5)

**35. GRID PATHWAYS**
Understanding turning through right angles. (S2)
Understanding congruence. (S4)
Planning work methodically. Recording systemmatically. (UA3/4/5)
Selecting materials and mathematics for a task. Checking and reveiwing progress. (UA3/4/5)

**36. JOINS**
Planning work methodically. Recording systemmatically. (UA3/4/5)
Selecting materials and mathematics for a task. Checking and reviewing progress. (UA3/4/5)

**37. PATHWAY LENGTHS**
Using metric units of length. (N2/3)
Using a centimetre ruler. (N3)

**38. DICE TOTALS**
Addition of single digit numbers. (N3/4)
Pattern in number. Addition patterns. (A2/3)
Working systemmatically. Checking and reviewing progress. (UA3/4/5)

**39. IMPOSSIBLE DICE**
Recognising rotations. (S2)
Recognising 2D representation of 3D objects. (S6)

**40/41. COME HOME**
Addition facts. (N2)
Planning methodically. Reviewing progress. (UA3/4/5)

**42/43. SHAPE RACE**
Recognising different shapes. (S2)
Sorting 2D shapes. (S3)

**44/45. MUSHROOM PICKING**
Addition, mentally, of two digit numbers. Estimating and approximating addition calculations. (N4)

**46. CALCULATOR LIGHTS**
Checking there is sufficient information. Working methodically and reviewing progress. (UA3/4/5)

**47. MISSING NUMBERS**
Solving number problems using a calculator. (N3/4)
Use of a symbol to stand for an unknown number. (A2)
Selecting the mathematics to use for a task. Planning methodically. (UA3/4)

**48. MISSING SIGNS**
Solving number problems using a calculator. (N3/4)
Selecting the mathematics to use for a task. Planning methodically. (UA3/4)

---

**NOTE:** References in parenthesis refer to the relevent part of the Curriculum, e.g. (N3) = Number, Level.

# Calculator Story

Use your calculator to perform these calculations.
Then turn the calculator upside down
to find the missing words.

**This is a story about _ _ _ _ .**          (2512 x 2) + 969

**My local shop _ _ _ _ _ _ them.**          60000 - 2265

**I prefer the   _ _ _   ones.**          459 x 2

**Sometimes I like to _ _ _ _ them.**          1777 x 4

**Sometimes I crack open the _ _ _ _ _ _ ,**          (110000 + 5469) x 5

**and then I fry them in   _ _ _  .**          71 x 10

**Sometimes I eat them raw,**

**but I also tell _ _ _ _ .**          6000 - 683

Which of these calculator numbers, upside down, look like letters?

Find some upside-down numbers which make words.

*Invent some calculations of your own which make missing words.*

# Memories

table        ant

ruler

teacher

dog              flower

apple

gate      girl      house

joke    mouse      toffee    sun

star    comic

Look at these words for 2 minutes.
Try to remember as many words as you can.
Then cover up the sheet and write down all the words you can remember.
Compare with your friends.
Which words were remembered by all of you?
Which words were easy to forget?
Draw graphs to illustrate your results.

★ *Invent your own sheet of words, and try it out on your friends.*
★ *Make a visual memories sheet.*
   *Collect magazine pictures and stick on a sheet.*

# Wordscore

Make 3 letter words only.

To find the **Wordscore**, look at the table and add up the numbers for each letter.

Examples: **top**  20 + 15 + 16  = 51
**bug**  2 + 21 + 7  = 30

Think of ten words of your own, write them in this table, then find their Wordscores.

**Wordscore**

| Word | Number | Wordscore |
|------|--------|-----------|
| 1. | | |
| 2. | | |
| 3. | | |
| 4. | | |
| 5. | | |
| 6. | | |
| 7. | | |
| 8. | | |
| 9. | | |
| 10. | | |

a = 1
b = 2
c = 3
d = 4
e = 5
f = 6
g = 7
h = 8
i = 9
j = 10
k = 11
l = 12
m = 13
n = 14
o = 15
p = 16
q = 17
r = 18
s = 19
t = 20
u = 21
v = 22
w = 23
x = 24
y = 25
z = 26

What is the smallest Wordscore you can find?
What is the largest Wordscore you can find?

★ *Draw another table.*
*Think of ten 4-letter words and find their Wordscores.*
*How many different words can you find which have a Wordscore between 20 and 30?*

# Word Lists

Here are two word lists.

## Animals

1. cat
2. dog
3. horse
4. hamster
5. pig
6. lion
7. donkey
8. giraffe
9. pony
10. tiger

## Birds

1. wren
2. robin
3. starling
4. thrush
5. eagle
6. parrot
7. puffin
8. blue tit
9. chaffinch
10. skylark

**Vowels are the letters a, e, i, o, u.**
Complete this table by counting how many times each vowel has been used in both lists. The letter 'o' has been done for you.

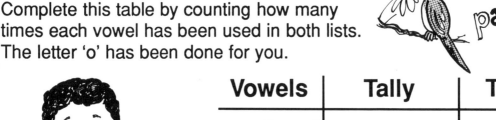

| Vowels | Tally | Total |
|---|---|---|
| a | | |
| e | | |
| i | | |
| o | ⦀⦀ ‖ | 7 |
| u | | |

Which vowel has been used the most times?
Which vowel has been used the fewest times?
Draw a bar graph to show the results.
Write about it.

*Invent your own word lists, and count how many times each vowel has been used. Compare the results and write about them. Which letter is used most often in English? Investigate the use of consonants (letters which aren't vowels).*

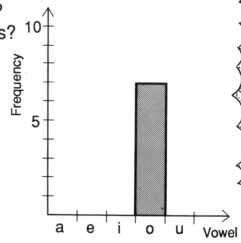

# Word Game

In the table, write down 20 words beginning with 'T'.
Score points for each word, based on the number of letters.

Examples: **train** - 5 points     **tea**     - 3 points
               **trip**  - 4 points     **tortoise** - 8 points

Find the total points for all the three lettered words, then the four lettered words, and so on. Use a calculator to find the overall total.

| Words | Points |
|---|---|
| 3  letter words | |
| 4  letter words | |
| 5  letter words | |
| 6  letter words | |
| 7  letter words | |
| 8  letter words | |
| Total | |

★ *Try again with a different starting letter.*

★ *Take any reading book or newspaper. Find the first 50 words beginning with a particular letter, and record the number of letters in each of those words. Which letter do you think that most words will start with? Write about your results.*

# Multiplication Square

| 1 | 2 | 3 | 4 | 5 | 6 | 7 | 8 | 9 | 10 |
|---|---|---|---|---|---|---|---|---|----|
| 2 | 4 | 6 | 8 | 10 | 12 | 14 | 16 | 18 | 20 |
| 3 | 6 | 9 | 12 | 15 | 18 | 21 | 24 | 27 | 30 |
| 4 | 8 | 12 | 16 | 20 | 24 | 28 | 32 | 36 | 40 |
| 5 | 10 | 15 | 20 | 25 | 30 | 35 | 40 | 45 | 50 |
| 6 | 12 | 18 | 24 | 30 | 36 | 42 | 48 | 54 | 60 |
| 7 | 14 | 21 | 28 | 35 | 42 | 49 | 56 | 63 | 70 |
| 8 | 16 | 24 | 32 | 40 | 48 | 56 | 64 | 72 | 80 |
| 9 | 18 | 27 | 36 | 45 | 54 | 63 | 72 | 81 | 90 |
| 10 | 20 | 30 | 40 | 50 | 60 | 70 | 80 | 90 | 100 |

This is a column.

This is a row.

Study this multiplication square.
Cover up this square and, without looking, try to say the numbers;

(a) in the second column

(b) in the fifth column

(c) in the fourth row

(d) in a diagonal.

What other line of numbers can you say without looking?
*Draw a blank 10 x 10 square, and see if you can complete it correctly.*
*Then use this sheet to check if you are correct.*

| 1 | 2 | 3 |  |  |  |  |  |  |  |  |  |  |
|---|---|---|--|--|--|--|--|--|--|--|--|--|
| 2 | 4 | 6 | 8 |  |  |  |  |  |  |  |  |  |
| 3 | 6 | 9 | 12 |  |  |  |  |  |  |  |  |  |
| 4 | 8 | 12 | 16 |  |  |  |  |  |  |  |  |  |
| 5 | 10 | 15 |  |  |  |  |  |  |  |  |  |  |

This is a 5 x 13 multiplication rectangle.
☆Copy and complete it.
☆Can you draw a 4 x 16 multiplication rectangle?
Try a 15 x 15 square.

# Missing Numbers

Study the multiplication square on sheet 10, note the patterns, and when you have finished, cover it up.

These are parts of the square which have been cut up, and numbers removed. See if you can write in the correct numbers.

☆ Invent some parts of the square of your own.
Draw the grids and put in two number clues for each.
Ask a friend to solve them.

# Cutting Up Squares

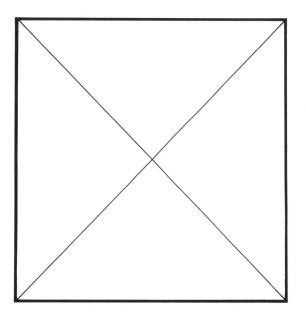

Draw a square on card.
Draw the diagonals.
Cut out the 4 pieces.
Make shapes by joining the pieces at equal edges.

This is how you might do it:

You can turn the pieces over if you like.

Use all the 4 pieces to make

 **a parallelogram**

**a right-angled triangle**

**a trapezium**

**a rectangle**

**a hexagon**

How many different shapes can you make with 2 of the pieces?
How many with 3 pieces?

★ *Experiment to see what shapes you can make with the pieces cut from each of these squares:*

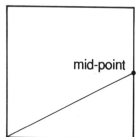
mid-point

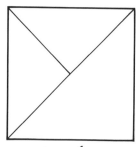

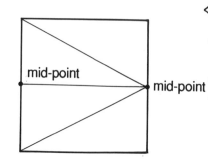
mid-point    mid-point

# Stars

You will need some large squares of paper.

21cm

30cm

Fold them in half, and in half again.

Draw a single straight line across the folded corner.
Cut along the line and open the paper out.
This will produce a piece —

and a hole —

Experiment to see what different shaped pieces and holes you can make.

Now try by drawing two lines.

See what different shapes you can make.
☆ *Make a display to show them.*

This page may be photocopied for classroom use only

# Square Shapes

Look at these shapes made by joining squares.

1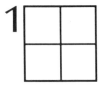
2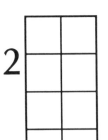
3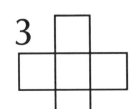
4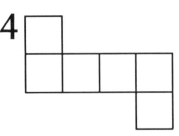

5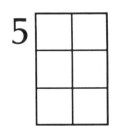
6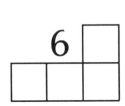
7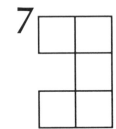
8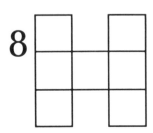

Write down for each shape:

a) **the area**

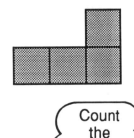

c) **the number of sides**

This is one side.

b) **the perimeter**

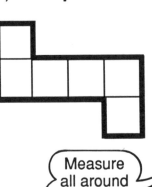

Count the squares.

Measure all around the edge.

★ Make your own shapes with squares. Join them edge to edge.
Draw the shapes you make.
Write down the area, perimeter and number of sides for each shape.

# Rows And Columns

Draw a large 4 x 4 square grid.

Make 16 cards to fit on to each small square.

Write numbers on the cards so that you have four 1s, four 2s, four 3s and four 4s.

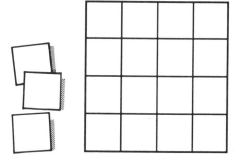

Arrange the cards on the square so that the same number does not appear in:

a) any row
b) any column
c) either diagonal.

Some clues are shown on the square.
☆ Record the result.

☆ *Try a similar activity by drawing a 5 x 5 square grid, and making 25 cards, four of each of the numbers 1, 2, 3, 4 and 5.*

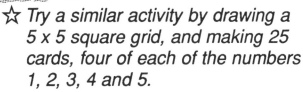

# Counter Arrangements

Use counters of two colours (red and yellow).
Arrange three of them on this **counter strip**.

 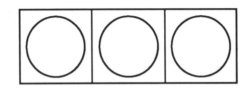  

Here are two arrangements.

How many different arrangements can you find?
Record them.

Find different counter
arrangements on these

 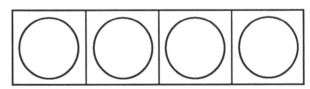

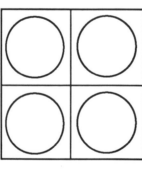

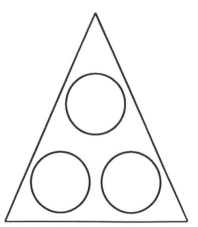

# Counter Shapes

You need a set of counters.
Take 16 counters.

Make these rectangles:

2 by 8

1 by 16

4 by 4

Now use 12 counters to make some different rectangles.
Record them by drawing round the counters or coints.

☆ *Try with 10 counters, 11 counters, and up to 20 counters.*
Which number will make the most arrangements?

# Reversals

These pairs of numbers are called **reversals**.

Add the pairs together.

15 + 51 = ___
38 + 83 = ___
24 + 42 = ___

Try some more.

13 + 31 = ___
18 + 81 = ___
52 + 25 = ___
58 + 85 = ___

☆ What do you notice?
☆ Does it always work?

Take away the smaller number from the larger number.

51 - 15 = ___
83 - 38 = ___
42 - 24 = ___

Try some more.

31 - 13 = ___
81 - 18 = ___
52 - 25 = ___
61 - 16 = ___
85 - 58 = ___

☆ What do you notice?
☆ Does it always work?

★ *Try some three digit numbers.*

163     361

# Rectangle Game

You need to cut 8 rectangles of this size from card.

This is a game for two players. Take turns to place a rectangle on the board, covering two squares. If you cannot go, you lose.

What is the smallest number of rectangles you can place on the board, and leave no room for another rectangle?

★ *Make new versions of the game on 5 x 5, and 6 x 6 boards.*

# Line-up

This is a game for two players.
One player has 12 red counters, the other 12 white counters.
Take turns to place a counter on an empty square on the board.

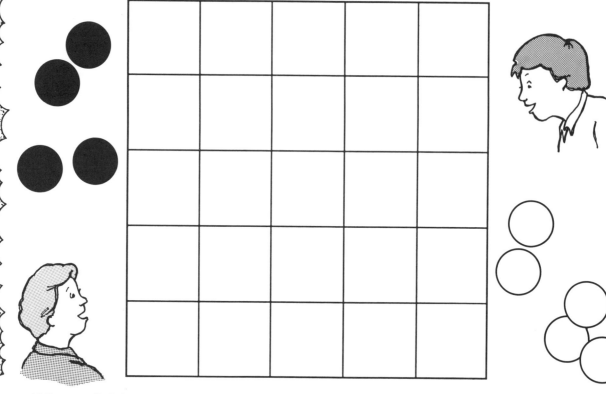

When all 24 counters have been placed:

☆ a straight line of **5** counters scores **3 points**;

☆ a straight line of **4** counters scores **2 points**;

☆ a straight line of **3** counters scores **1 point**.

The winner is the player with the most points.

Make your score chart:

> ___ lines of 5 counters =  ___
> ___ lines of 4 counters =  ___
> ___ lines of 3 counters =  ___
>                  Total =  ___

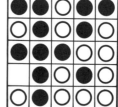

**Example:**

● has 1 line of 5 counters  = **3 points**
2 lines of 4 counters = **4 points**
1 line of 3 counters  = **1 point**
Total  = **7 points**

How many points does ○ have?

★ *Now make a 6 x 6 board and play with 18 counters each.*

# Birthday Month

Find a calendar for the month which contains your birthday.

Write the month and dates in here:

| Month _____ | | | | | | |
|---|---|---|---|---|---|---|
| **Mon** | **Tu** | **Wed** | **Th** | **Fri** | **Sat** | **Sun** |
| | | | | | | |
| | | | | | | |
| | | | | | | |
| | | | | | | |
| | | | | | | |

What day of the week is your birthday?

Do you know any other people who have a birthday in the same month? Mark these on your calendar month.

Complete the calendar here for the month after your birthday.

Mark any birthdays or special days.

| Month _____ | | | | | | |
|---|---|---|---|---|---|---|
| **Mon** | **Tu** | **Wed** | **Th** | **Fri** | **Sat** | **Sun** |
| | | | | | | |
| | | | | | | |
| | | | | | | |
| | | | | | | |
| | | | | | | |

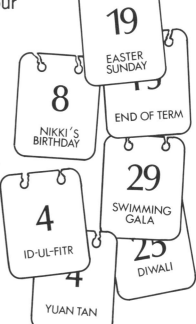

19 EASTER SUNDAY

8 NIKKI'S BIRTHDAY

END OF TERM

4 ID-UL-FITR

29 SWIMMING GALA

25 DIWALI

4 YUAN TAN

★ Write three things which are different about these two months.
Write three things which are the same about the two months.

★ *Ask 20 people what their birthday months are.*
*Describe the results.*

# Calendar Gaps

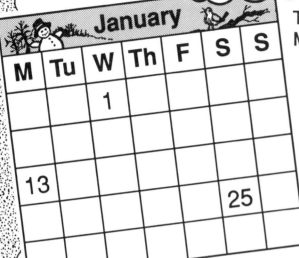

These calendar months have missing dates.
Mark the following dates on each month:

5, 12, 23, 28, 17, 2, 9.

☆ Next, fill in 7, 14, 21, 26, 30, 4.

**January**

| M | Tu | W | Th | F | S | S |
|---|----|----|----|----|----|----|
|   |    | 1  |    |    |    |    |
|   |    |    |    |    |    |    |
| 13 |   |    |    |    |    | 25 |
|   |    |    |    |    |    |    |

**February**

| M | Tu | W | Th | F | S | S |
|---|----|----|----|----|----|----|
|   |    |    |    |    | 1  |    |
|   |    |    |    |    |    |    |
| 10 |   |    |    |    |    |    |
|   | 25 |   |    |    |    |    |
|   |    |    |    |    |    |    |

**March**

| M | Tu | W | Th | F | S | S |
|---|----|----|----|----|----|----|
|   |    |    |    |    |    | 1  |
|   | 4  |    |    |    |    |    |
|   |    |    |    |    |    |    |
|   | 25 |   |    |    |    |    |
|   |    |    |    |    |    |    |

**May**

| M | Tu | W | Th | F | S | S |
|---|----|----|----|----|----|----|
|   |    |    |    | 1  |    |    |
|   |    |    |    |    |    |    |
|   |    |    |    | 15 |    |    |
|   |    |    |    |    |    |    |
| 25 |   |    |    |    |    |    |

| M | Tu | W | Th | F | S | S |
|---|----|----|----|----|----|----|
|   |    |    |    |    |    |    |
|   |    |    |    |    |    |    |
|   |    |    |    |    |    |    |
|   |    |    |    |    |    |    |
|   |    |    |    |    |    |    |

☆ Now complete them.

☆ In January, colour the even numbers.
☆ In February, colour the odd numbers.
☆ In March, colour the multiples of 3.
☆ In May, colour the multiples of 4.

☆ Describe the patterns each time.

◁ *Choose your own month and colouring rule on this calendar.*

# Calendar Jigsaw

This calendar month was cut up by mistake.
Cut out the pieces and fit it together again.

What is the first day of the month?
What day is the second day of the month?
How many Wednesdays are in the month?

**Calendar challenge:**

*Make your own drawing of a calendar month on squared paper. Then cut it into a jigsaw and ask a friend to piece it together.*

# Diagonals

Here is a 2 x 2 square for the calendar month.

```
 6  7
13 14
```
(20)    (20)

The diagonals both total 20.

$6 + 14 = 20$

$13 + 7 = 20$

| April 1992 | | | | | | |
|---|---|---|---|---|---|---|
| M | Tu | W | Th | F | S | S |
|  |  | 1 | 2 | 3 | 4 | 5 |
| 6 | 7 | 8 | 9 | 10 | 11 | 12 |
| 13 | 14 | 15 | 16 | 17 | 18 | 19 |
| 20 | 21 | 22 | 23 | 24 | 25 | 26 |
| 27 | 28 | 29 | 30 |  |  |  |

The diagonal totals for these 2 x 2 squares are given.
Look at the calendar month to find the missing numbers and write them in.

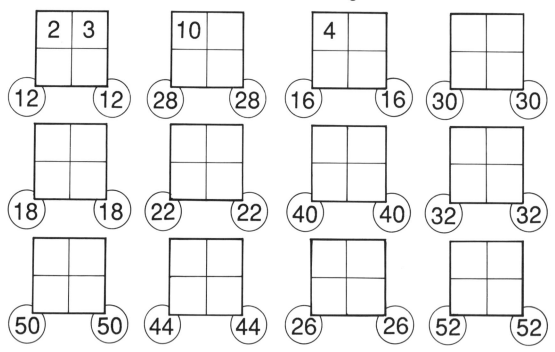

Now find both row totals for each square.
What do you notice?
Do the same for the column totals for each square also.
*Choose your own calendar month. Find all the 2 x 2 squares you can.*
*Investigate the row and column totals.*

# Rectangle Corners

## May 1992

| M | Tu | W | Th | F | S | S |
|---|----|----|----|---|---|---|
|   |    |    |    | 1 | 2 | 3 |
| 4 | 5  | 6  | 7  | 8 | 9 | 10 |
| 11 | 12 | 13 | 14 | 15 | 16 | 17 |
| 18 | 19 | 20 | 21 | 22 | 23 | 24 |
| 25 | 26 | 27 | 28 | 29 | 30 | 31 |

Here is a 2 x 3 rectangle from this month's calendar.

It is a 31 rectangle, because the opposite corners total 31.

$$11 + 20 = 31$$
$$18 + 13 = 31$$

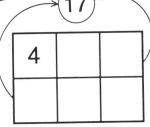

Write in the numbers in these rectangles.

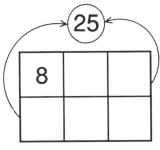

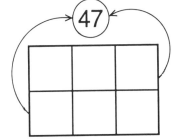

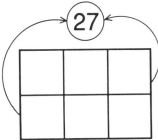

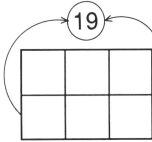

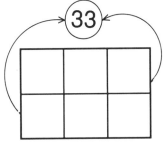

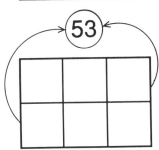

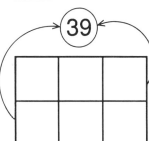

★ Look at this month's calendar.

☆ See how many different totals you can find for the opposite corners of a 2 x 3 rectangle. Record your results.

# Calendar Totals

**September 1992**

| M | Tu | W | Th | F | S | S |
|---|----|----|----|----|----|----|
|   | 1  | 2  | 3  | 4  | 5  | 6  |
| 7 | 8  | 9  | 10 | 11 | 12 | 13 |
| 14 | 15 | 16 | 17 | 18 | 19 | 20 |
| 21 | 22 | 23 | 24 | 25 | 26 | 27 |
| 28 | 29 | 30 |   |   |   |   |

Choose four different 3 x 3 squares from this calendar month, and write them in these squares.
One has been done for you.

| 8 | 9 | 10 |
|---|---|----|
| 15 | 16 | 17 |
| 22 | 23 | 24 |

Find these totals for each of your squares:

a) First diagonal

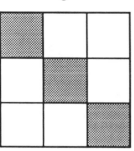

b) Second diagonal

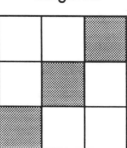

c) Middle row

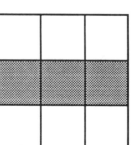

d) Middle column

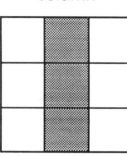

☆ *Record your results and write about anything you discover.*
*Repeat the activity with a different month - this month, for example.*

# Three Circles

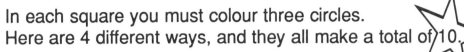

In each square you must colour three circles.
Here are 4 different ways, and they all make a total of 10.

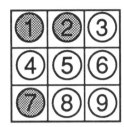 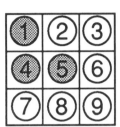 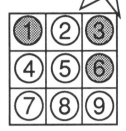 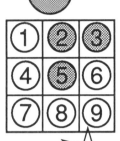

Find 6 different ways of colouring three circles which make a total of 12.

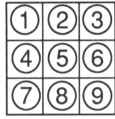 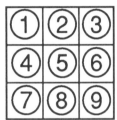 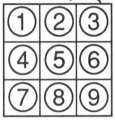

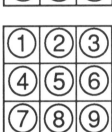 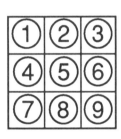 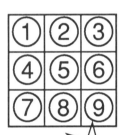

Find 6 different ways of colouring three circles which make a total of 18.

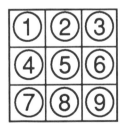 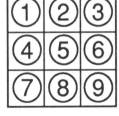 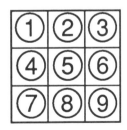

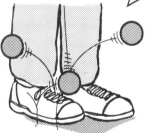

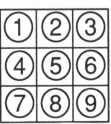 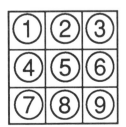

Draw some more sets of circles like these and see how many ways you can find of colouring three circles to make totals of 20.

☆ *Repeat for some different totals of your own choice.*

# Three In A Line

This is a game for three players.

You need three dice, and some counters each.
Take turns to throw the three dice and find the total of any two of them.
Place a counter on any circle which matches this total.
The winner is the first player to have 3 counters in a straight line.

☆ *Play the game by aiming to have 4 counters in a straight line.*

# Making Numbers

Try to find different ways of 'Making 3'.

Find 3 different ways using addition.
Find 3 different ways using subtraction.
Find 3 different ways using division.

Complete the table.  Some have been done for you.

### Making 3

| Addition | Subtraction | Division |
|----------|-------------|----------|
| 0 + 3 | 7 - 4 | 9 ÷ 3 |
| 1 + 1 + 1 | | |
| | | |

Now see if you can find five different ways of 'Making 5'.

### Making 5

| Addition | Subtraction | Division |
|----------|-------------|----------|
| | | |
| | | |
| | | |
| | | |
| | | |

*Choose your own number to make.*
*See how many ways you can find of making it.*

This page may be photocopied for classroom use only

# Three Stamps

There are 6 different coloured stamps.

A **red** stamp costs     3p.
A **green** stamp costs     4p.
A **yellow** stamp costs     5p.
A **blue** stamp costs     6p.
A **pink** stamp costs     7p.
An **orange** stamp costs     8p.

Find the cost of postage for each of these letters.

①     ②     ③

④     ⑤     ⑥

⑦     ⑧     ⑨

★ How much change would you have from 30p for each letter?

★ How much change from 25p?

★ What is the total cost for all the letters?

★ How many different postage costs are possible using any three of these stamps?

# Three More Stamps

There are 6 different stamps in Gapland.

A **black** stamp costs    1p.
A **grey** stamp costs    2p.
A **green** stamp costs    3p.
A **yellow** stamp costs    4p.
A **red** stamp costs    5p.
A **brown** stamp costs    6p.

Each of these letters needs 3 different stamps.
For each envelope, look at the cost of postage and colour the 3 stamps to match this cost.

## postage 6p
① 
Mr P. GAP
12 GAP STREET
GAPTOWN
GAPLAND

## postage 9p
② 
Ms. Olive Oil
Popeye House
Spinachville
GAPLAND.

## postage 8p
③ 
Ivor Gap
2 High Street
DENTAL BRIDGE
GAPLAND

## postage 10p
④ 
Mr Teddy Bear
Honey Lane
Woodside
GAPLAND

## postage 14p
⑤ 
Cindy Doll
Wooden House
Toytown
GAPLAND

## postage 7p
⑥ 
Ellie Phant
Grey Street
Big Town
GAPLAND

## postage 11p
⑦ 
Fred Flintstone
Stonewell Cottage
Stonehenge
GAPLAND

## postage 15p
⑧ 
B. Simpson
Brat Street
Bratville
GAPLAND

## postage 12p
⑨ 
Chip Monk
Friar Lane
Abbotstown
GAPLAND

☆ Can any of these envelopes have a different set of three stamps?

# Three Digits

On each line you make a three digit number by choosing any three of these four digits.

| 5 | 2 | 7 | 8 |
|---|---|---|---|

Example: | 5 | 7 | 2 |   This shows the 3 digit number 572.

On the first line, for example, you try to make the largest 3 digit number you can.

1.  Largest number.

2.  Smallest number.

3.  Largest odd number.

4.  Smallest odd number.

5.  Largest even number.

6.  Smallest even number.

7.  Nearest number to 400.

8.  Nearest number to 600.

9.  Nearest number to 300.

10. Nearest number to 550.

☆ *Try again with a different set of 4 digits to choose from.*

# Three Darts

You can throw 3 darts at this dartboard:
what is the largest possible score?

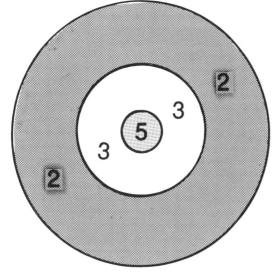

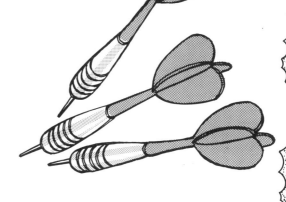

How many
different scores are possible?

Now see how many different scores are possible when 3 darts are
thrown at this board.

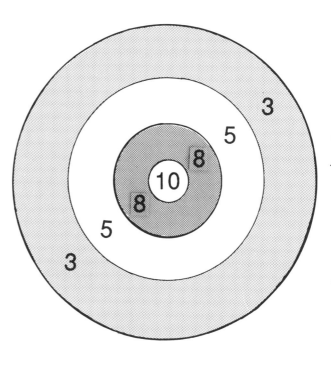

★ *Invent your own dartboard and explore possible scores using 3 darts.*

This page may be photocopied for classroom use only

# Stepping Stones

Find a pathway from START to END which makes 7.

☆ Can you find two different pathways which make 8?
☆ Which pathway makes the largest number?
☆ Which pathway makes the smallest number?
☆ How many different pathways can you find?

Find a pathway from START to END which totals 15.

☆ Can you find three different pathways which total 16?
☆ Mark the pathway which makes the largest number in **red**.
☆ Mark the pathway which makes the smallest number in **green**.

★ *Make your own stepping stones puzzle, writing different numbers on the stones. Find some different pathways.*

# Grid Pathways

Start with a 3 x 4 grid.
Shade a starting square, then try to draw a
pathway which passes through every square
once and once only.

✳ **No diagonal moves are allowed.**

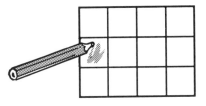

Here are two pathways from different starting points:

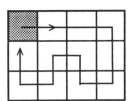  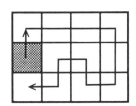

Try starting at other squares, and draw them here.
Practise on squared paper first.

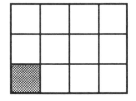  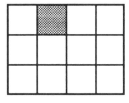  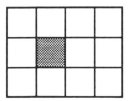  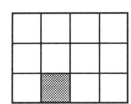

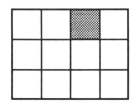  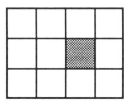  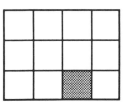  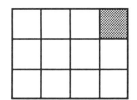

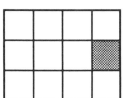  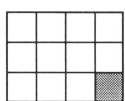  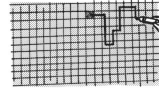

☆ *Invent a different sized grid and try to find pathways by
starting at different squares.*

# Joins

Use a ruler to draw straight lines from each dot to every other dot. How many lines have you drawn?

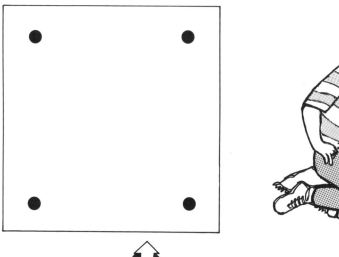

**Number of lines = ___**

Now try these:

**Number of lines = ___**

**Number of lines = ___**

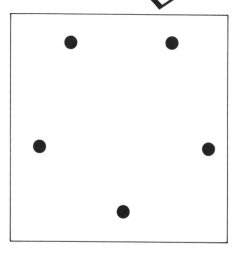
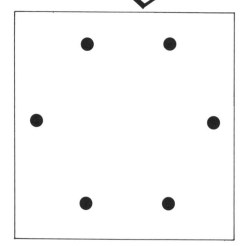

Colour a pattern in your drawings.

☆ *Invent your own set of dots. Guess how many lines you can draw, then draw them to see how close your guess is.*

# Pathway Lengths

This is a game for two players.
Take turns to throw two dice.
Look on the chart below for the numbers thrown.

Draw a line with a ruler to join the two numbers.
Measure the line to the nearest centimetre.
This is your score.
You do not score if the numbers are already joined.
The winner is the player with the highest score
after 10 throws.

**Keep score:**

| Gary | Carla |
|------|-------|
| 5 | 3 |
| 6 | |

•4          •2          •5

1•

•3

                    1•

              •4

•3

              •5

                         •6

      6•

# Dice Totals

You need 3 dice.
Place them so that the total showing is 11.

Can you find six different ways of making
a total of 11?
Record them here.

Find five different ways of making a total of 13,

6 + 3 + ...

and three different ways of making a total of 15.

See how many ways you can find of making other totals.

☆ *Now try different ways of making totals using 4 dice.*

# Impossible Dice

This is a net for a dice.

One view of the dice is:

Which of these drawings are also views of the same dice, and which are impossible? You can use a dice to help you.

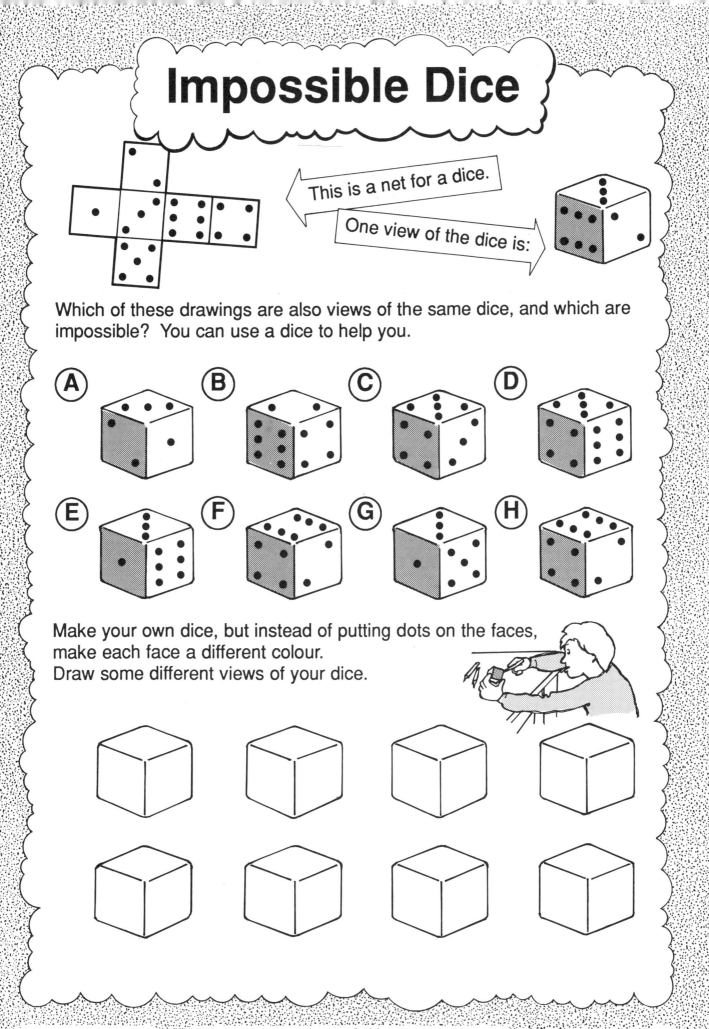

(A)   (B)   (C)   (D)

(E)   (F)   (G)   (H)

Make your own dice, but instead of putting dots on the faces, make each face a different colour.
Draw some different views of your dice.

# Come Home

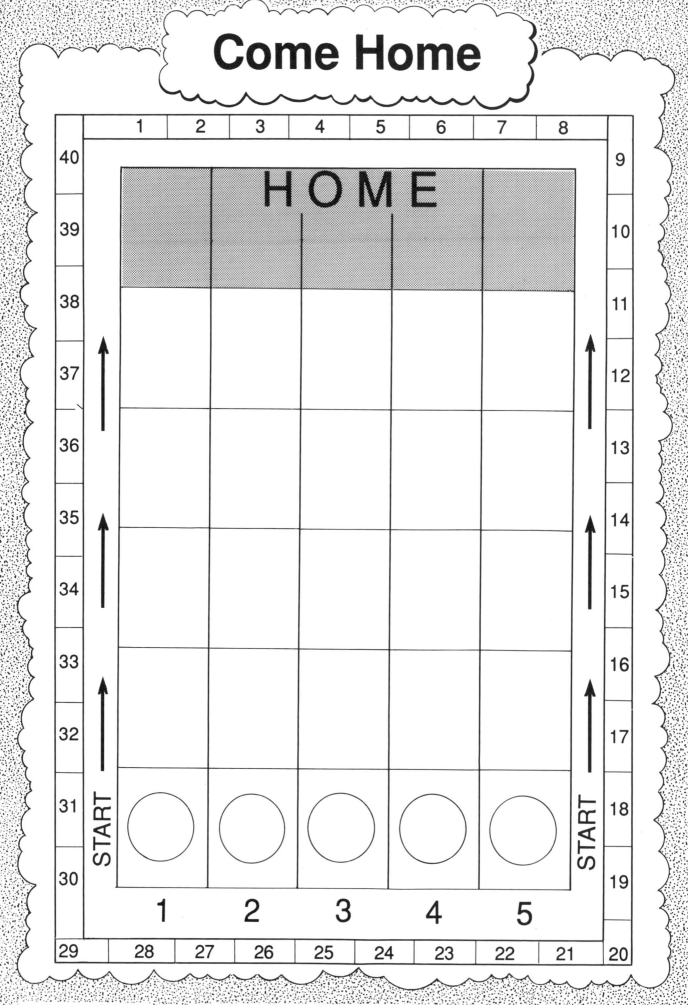

# Come Home
## Teacher's Page

**Teacher Note**: Duplicate these rules if you wish, or just read them out.

You need one dice.
Place five counters, one on each of the starting circles.
Throw the dice and move counters according to the dice numbers.
For example, if you throw a [dice showing 5] this means you can move:

the 5 counter one space forward
OR the 1 counter five spaces forward
OR the 4 counter and 1 counter each one space forward
OR the 3 counter and 2 counter each one space forward.

Each time you throw the dice, tick a box, in turn, around the outside of the board. This will tell you how many throws you have had.
See how many throws it takes you to get all counters home.
This is your score.
Try again for a smaller score.

---

**Teacher Note**: Try this extension activity with more-able children.

Make a larger board for this 'Come Home' game.

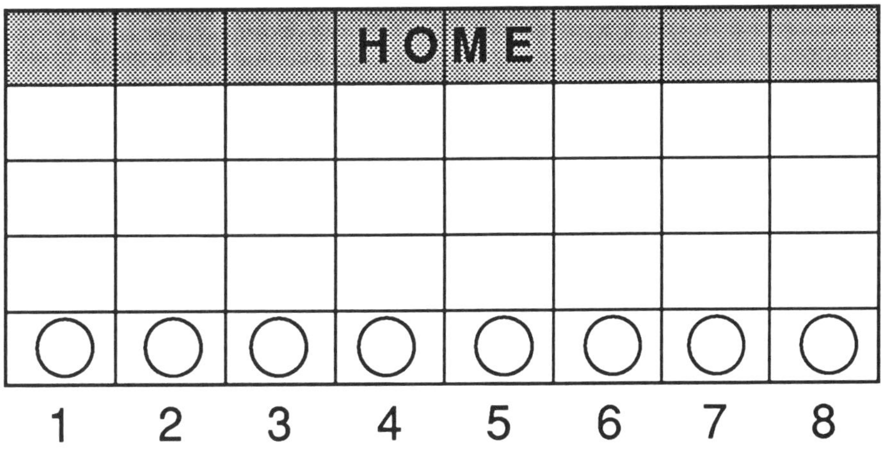

| | | | H | O | M | E | | |
|---|---|---|---|---|---|---|---|---|
| | | | | | | | | |
| | | | | | | | | |
| | | | | | | | | |
| ◯ | ◯ | ◯ | ◯ | ◯ | ◯ | ◯ | ◯ | |

  1    2    3    4    5    6    7    8

You need a pack of cards.
Let Jack = 11, Queen = 12, King = 13.
Instead of throwing a dice, shuffle the cards, place them in a face-down pile, and turn them over, one at a time.
You have to get all 8 counters home. Count how many cards you need.

# Shape Dice

Glue or photocopy this page on to a piece of card.

Cut along the heavy lines.
Score along the dotted lines.
Glue the tabs.
Colour each shape.

What are the shapes called?

Don't cut off the tabs!

# Shape Race

This is a game for two players, each with a counter.
You need the shape dice made from page 42.
Each player places a counter at 'Start'.

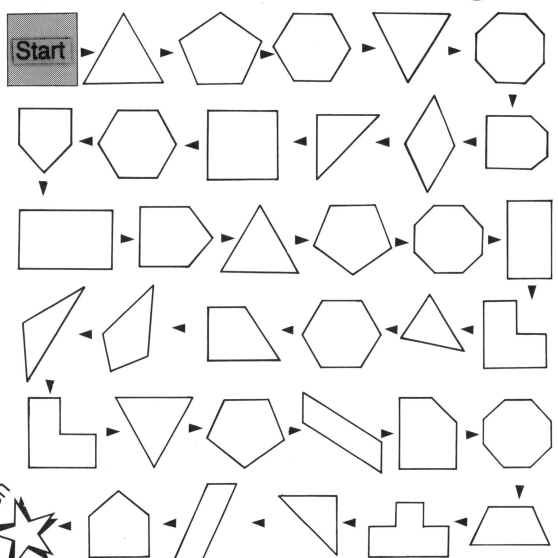

Throw the shape dice and move forward according to the number of sides on the shape showing on the dice.

Example:     move  3

If you land on a shape which has the same number of sides as the shape on the shape dice, then go back 5 spaces (or back to the 'Start').
The winner is the first player to reach or pass 'Finish'.

# Mushroom Picking

This page may be photocopied for classroom use only

# Mushroom Picking

This is a game for 2 players.
- ☆ Take turns to choose any two of these numbers.
- ☆ Add them together using a calculator.
- ☆ If you can find the answer on a mushroom, then pick it by placing a counter on top of it.
- ☆ The winner is the first player to pick 8 mushrooms.

| A 23 | B 17 | C 14 | D 31 |
|------|------|------|------|

| E 9 | F 27 | G 17 |
|-----|------|------|

| H 34 | I 18 |
|------|------|

## ★ Mushroom Picking Challenge

This is a challenge for one person.
- ★ Start by placing a counter on every mushroom.

- ★ Remove any one counter.

- ★ Then see if you can find the two numbers which add together to make the mushroom number.

- ★ Repeat for 10 mushrooms altogether.

- ★ How many did you get right?

# Calculator Lights

Any digit is displayed by using up to 7 lights.

3 uses five lights.

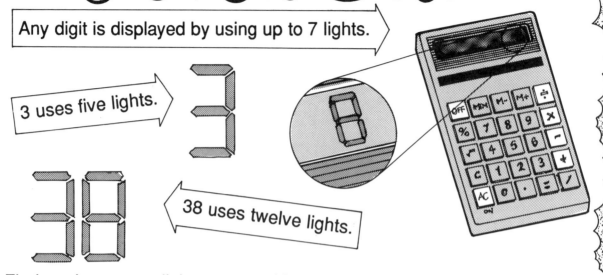

38 uses twelve lights.

Find out how many lights are used by other numbers.

Can you find some different two digit numbers which can all be made using ten lights?
Draw them here.

How many can you find altogether?
How many can you find using twelve lights?
Which three digit numbers can be made using ten lights?

# Missing Numbers

Use a calculator to help you write in the missing numbers in the boxes.

First try to find them without a calculator.

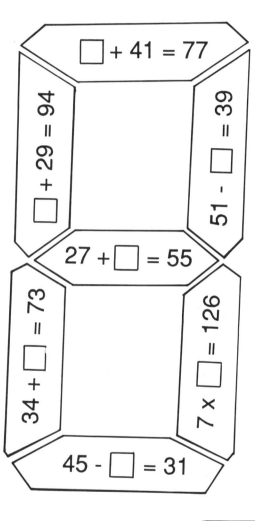

☐ + 41 = 77

☐ + 29 = 94

51 - ☐ = 39

27 + ☐ = 55

34 + ☐ = 73

7 x ☐ = 126

45 - ☐ = 31

34 + ☐ = 104

☐ = 72 (9 x ☐ = 72)

52 + ☐ = 89

15 x ☐ = 60

☐ + 29 = 57

83 - ☐ = 35

7 x ☐ = 84

Colour all the sections which contain an EVEN missing number. e.g. 36 + 41 = 77

These are lights on a calculator number. What calculator number have you coloured?

☆ Invent a **missing numbers** page of your own.

# Missing Signs

Use a calculator to help you write in EITHER a '+' OR a 'x' sign in the empty boxes.

First try to find them without a calculator.

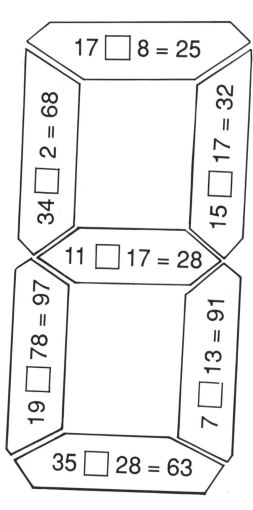

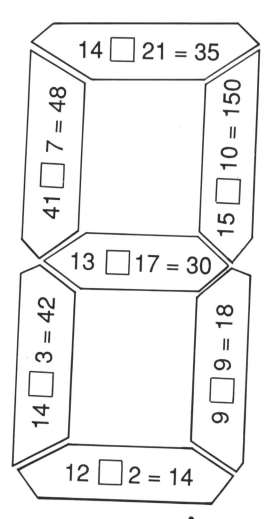

Colour all the sections which contain a missing '+' sign.

These are lights on a calculator number.
What calculator number have you coloured?

☆ Invent your own **missing signs** page.